For Gabe,

"Defend Nature & Animals!"

(signature)

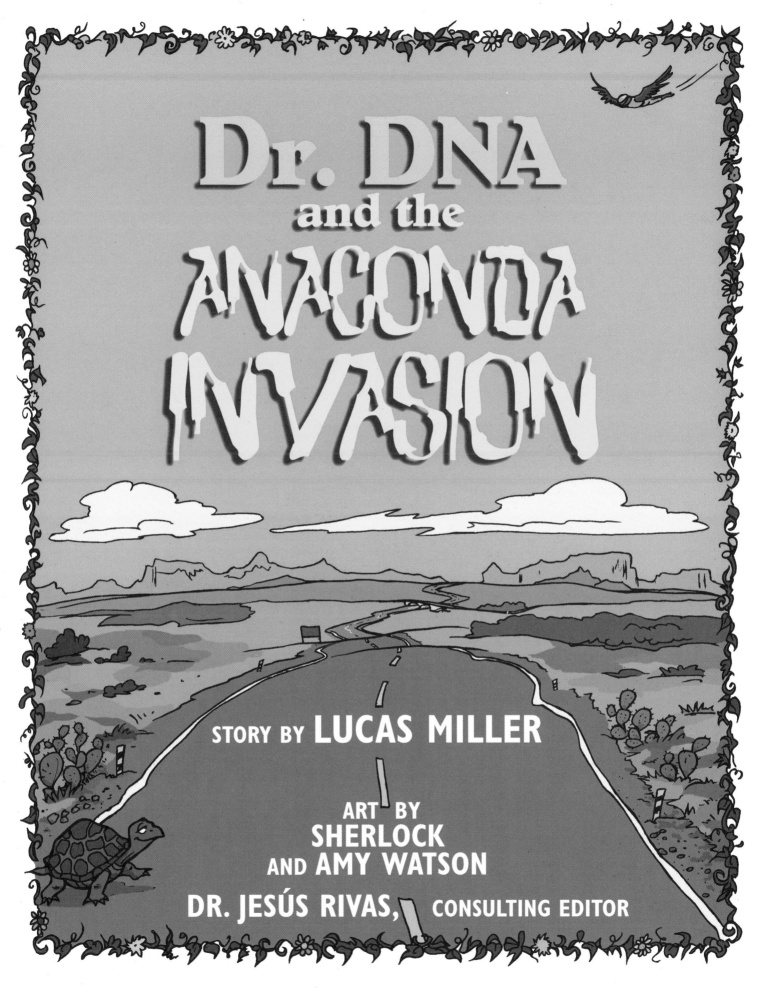

Dr. DNA
and the
ANACONDA INVASION

STORY BY **LUCAS MILLER**

ART BY
SHERLOCK
AND **AMY WATSON**

DR. JESÚS RIVAS, CONSULTING EDITOR

BioRhythms Publishing, Austin, Texas, USA

This book is dedicated to the real superheroes for animals—the scientists, educators, conservationists and other folks working to keep things WILD!!

Printed in Canada on 100% post-consumer, recycled paper by Marquis Bookprinting, Inc.

Cover and graphic layout by Sherlock, Amy Watson & Edie Weinberg

Edited by Harold Underdown, www.underdown.org

BioRhythms Publishing would like to thank Dr. Jesús Rivas of the Anaconda Project for his time and contributions to this book. Lucas Miller offers his sincerest gratitude to Sherlock and Amy Watson for their tremendous patience and creativity. He also thanks his family, friends, and fans for all their support over the years.

BioRhythms Publishing
6306 Nasco Drive, Suite 101
Austin, TX 78757

First impression

ISBN: 0-9789139-0-6

ISBN13: 978-0-9789139-0-8

Library of Congress Control Number: 2006907982

PHOTO CREDITS:
p.30 and 31 top and middle © 2006 bottom Paul Raffaele
p.31 bottom © 2006 Peter Arnold, Inc. / Alamy

* Whitaker, P.B. and R. Shine. 2000. "Sources of mortality of large elapid snakes in an agricultural landscape." --Journal of Herpetology 34:721-128.

26

Meet Dr. Jesús Rivas—this guy's REALLY helping anacondas!

He can't sprout wings, transform into a snake or chat with capybaras but Dr. Rivas is the closest thing to a superhero the green anaconda has!

At age 16, Jesús became a fireman in Venezuela. The station often received calls about snakes intruding on people's property and it was "Rivas to the rescue!" Venomous or not, he would capture the trouble-making serpents and return them to their habitats.

Hoping to better help his reptilian friends, Rivas went on to become a zoologist, or animal scientist. Since 1992, he has led the Anaconda Project, a field study of the world's heaviest snake. "They're famous," he recalls, "but when we began, there had been no dedicated study of them in the wild." He set to work uncovering the basics about anacondas: their diet, predators, size, reproduction and other facts.

He and his team searched for anacondas in the llanos, or grassy floodplains, along the Orinoco River in Venezuela. They have recorded length, weight and other data of over 900 individual snakes!

¡Ay! That story was ridículo! I think we need to tell the REAL story about anacondas!

You tell 'em, Dr. Rivas!

So, how big do anacondas get?

"In our study," Dr. Rivas says, "we found female anacondas, which are much larger than the males, averaged about 13 feet and 70 pounds. The greatest length and weight we've recorded are 18 feet and 220 pounds."

But what about those tales of giant anacondas, 30 feet or more in length?

"I've heard so many false reports about anacondas," he replies, "that I only believe measurements I've taken myself. I do not doubt, however, that there are anacondas much larger than the ones we've been able to capture in our study."

What do they eat?

Capybaras are, indeed, common prey but Rivas and his crew have also observed them eating birds, lizards, turtles, deer, caimans (a relative of the alligator) and many more species.

How do they find and capture prey?

Anacondas identify prey primarily by scent which they detect with their forked tongues. That means that no anaconda would mistake a guy in a costume for a real capybara!

Even if it did, anacondas are so slow on land that they would never chase after prey. They hunt from the water and use their camouflage to help them surprise attack when prey is within striking distance.

Anacondas have no venom nor do they crush the bones of their prey. Their powerful coils make it impossible for their prey to draw a breath and virtually stop its blood circulation.

Don't anacondas prey on people?

"It is possible but there are actually no documented accounts of it," Rivas states. "If it happens at all, it's quite rare because people and anacondas prefer different kinds of environments and they rarely encounter one another. In truth, people are much more likely to attack an anaconda than vice versa."

Would capybara numbers really skyrocket if anacondas disappeared?

They would likely increase but certainly not as ridiculously as they did in the story. You see, jaguars and caimans also eat capybaras and they'd keep the "herbivore fiesta" from getting so outrageously out of hand.

Still, it is true that large predators, like anacondas, really do play key roles in maintaining the health and balance of their native ecosystems. If a predator goes extinct, problems will likely follow and an unhealthy environment is much more dangerous to us than any predator!

Rivas hopes that the Anaconda Project will help people better manage the wetlands of South America to help conserve anacondas and all the species that live there. So, no, he doesn't have a cape or spiffy goggles but Dr. Jesús Rivas is doing his best to save anacondas!

There's more about Dr. Rivas, anacondas and other animals at FunkySkunkies.com. Check it out and get started on your own zoological odyssey!

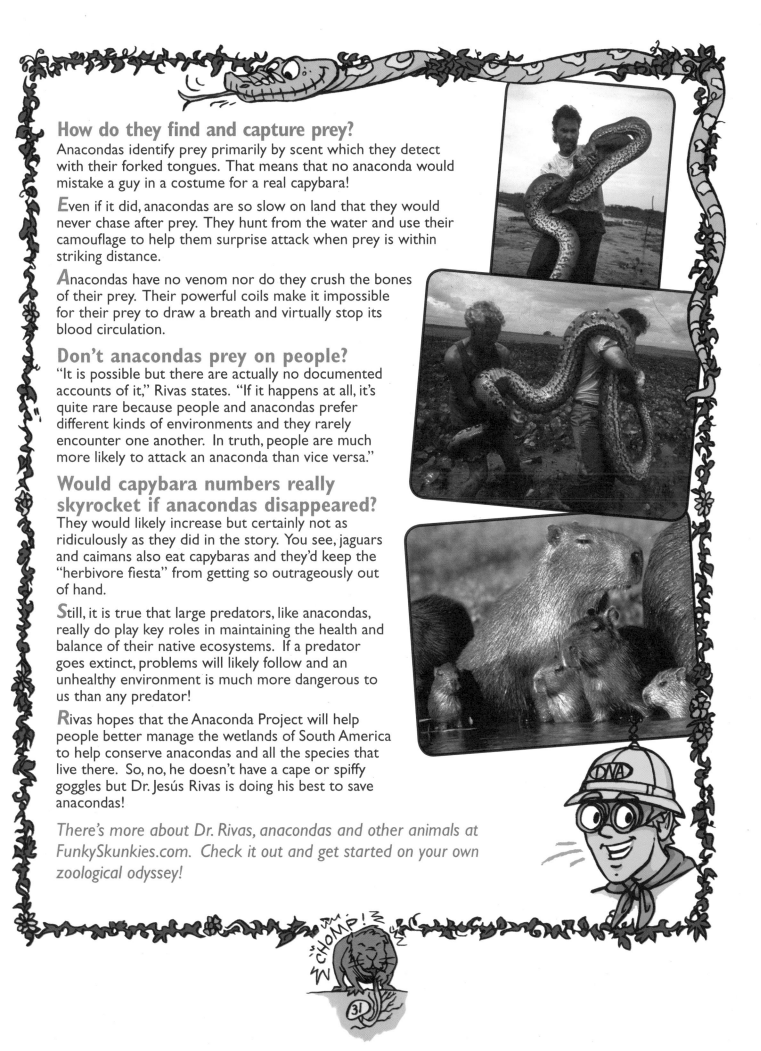

CHOMP!

31

Lucas Miller was driving down a country road one day when he saw a turtle crossing the road. He pulled over and helped her across, as he always does, but this time it got him thinking. "I already had an idea for a character who was a superhero for animals," he recalls, "and I figured that he would whisk a turtle out of harm's way just to get warmed up in the morning." Further inspired by children's infatuation with his song *The Anaconda La Bamba*, he began putting the pieces of this story together.

Lucas earned a degree in zoology from Miami University and has performed for over one million children. Blending stories, songs, humor and science, Lucas is also the author of *Fifi the Ferocious* and has created three, award-winning CD's.

He and his wife, Margalo, are raising their children in Austin, Texas.

Visit www.lucasmiller.net to sample his other works and learn about his school author visits.

Sherlock

Mild-mannered Leon Valley library clerk by day, sci-fi/fantasy/ humor artist by night, "Sherlock" (a.k.a. Sherry Watson) achieved a University *summa cum laude* BFA in drawing, and then scribbled the rest of her life away. She's drawn a few clip art collections, illustrated a book or two and snagged a Hugo nomination among other things.

A few of her latest doings include a music CD cover, an animé character doll, illustrations for Jonathan Frid's digital King *Richard III* project, a large painting of Elvis, some t-shirt designs, fun signs, funny animal covers for Colorado Book Associates' catalogs and cartoons of dragons and such for conventions.

Amy Watson

has a Bachelor's degree in Engineering and works in digital and print media doing editing, website design, and writing and illustrating comics. She also does commercial graphics and illustrations using a combination of traditional and digital methods.

Amy's overstuffed, overspoiled chow-mix, Paddington, served as the inspiration for the many, feasting capybaras in this story.